Rocky was at home with his mother.
'Look at this,' she said.
'This was at the other house.
This was when we went to get Max.'

1

'What is this?' asked Rocky.
'That is Max playing inside my cake tin,'
said his mother.
'Woof!' said Max.

2

'How old is Max?' asked Rocky.
'Now, let me see,' said his mother.
'Max is about two.
Yes, Max is two in two days.'

'Can we have a birthday party for Max?'
Rocky asked his mother.
She smiled.
'Do you want a birthday party, Max?'
she asked.
'Woof, woof!' said Max.

4

Two days later, Rocky came in.
He saw that his mother had made a cake.
'What a lovely cake!' said Rocky.
'Is it all for Max?'
'Woof, woof!' said Max.
'No, it is not for Max,' said his mother.
'Cake is not good for dogs.
The cake is for you children.'

Jamila came to the party.
'Happy birthday, Max.
This is for you,' she said.
'Woof, woof!' said Max.
'It is a tin of dog food,'
Jamila said to Rocky.

Rocky said to Max,
'You can have the dog food when
we have the cake.'

Tony and Tessa came to the party.
'Happy birthday, Max.
We've bought this for you,' they said.
'Woof, woof!' said Max.

'This is a good party,' said Tessa.
'I like this cake,' said Jamila.
'Yes, it's lovely cake,' said Tony.
Rocky gave Max his dog food.
'Woof, woof!' said Max.

The children all sang 'Happy birthday' to Max.
But Max was not happy.
He wanted some cake.

10

The children all went outside with
Rocky and his mother.
Max was on his own – with the cake.
Max jumped up onto the table.
He grabbed what was left of the cake.

Rocky came in with his mother.
She shouted at Max.
'Get down, Max!
Get off the table!'
Max jumped off the table.

They looked at the table.
There was no cake on the table.
They looked at Max.
'Did you take the cake?'
Rocky asked Max.
'Woof, woof!' said Max.

Tessa came in.

'I wanted some cake,' said Tessa.

'Have you put it in the cake tin?'

'No,' said Rocky.

'The cake is not inside the tin.

The cake is inside Max!'

Later Max lay down.
He was not happy.
His tail did not wag.
His inside was moving around!
It hurt!

'We said that cake was not
a good food for dogs,' said Rocky.
'Get out.
Go in the shed!'
Max made a strange sound...
'Woof, woof!'